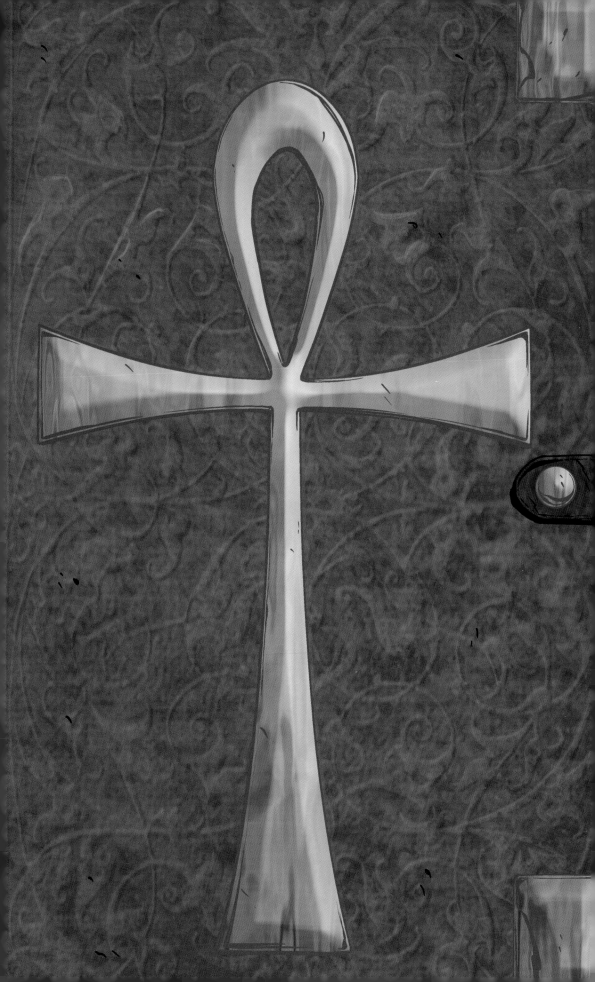

CHAPTER ①

My good son: this book-any book-is only a beginning. There are stories beyond what I can unfold here. Tales that go back before I can ever remember. But, what you already know can help you with the unknown.

THAT'S THE REACTION I WAS LOOKING FOR. ONE SHOT DEAL THOUGH. IT GOES BACK TOMORROW.

DON'T RETURN IT.

YOU SLAPPING TWO G'S IN MY HAND, SO I CAN HOLD ONTO THIS, COUNSELOR?

METRO INSTITUTE of ANTIQUITIES **PRIVATE AUCTION**

ON SECOND THOUGHT, MAYBE WE CAN FIND A KNOCK-OFF.

WOW, ELIJAH, THAT WAS ALMOST ROMANTIC.

OPEN MIC HERE, PEOPLE.

SORRY.

MY BAD.

THIS IS RECON, NOT PROJECT RUNWAY.

I WANT THAT DRESS.

YOU DON'T HAVE THE HIPS FOR IT.

I DO TOO.

LOOK YOU TWO, FOCUS SO WE CAN MAKE SURE THAT DRESS YOU COVET SO MUCH DOESN'T GET ANY BULLET HOLES IN IT.

I'M HEADING OVER.

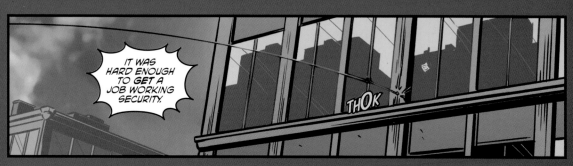

THOUGH I DON'T SEE WHY YOU COULDN'T HAVE GOTTEN *ME* AN INVITATION.

WHOOSH

IT WAS HARD ENOUGH TO *GET* A JOB WORKING SECURITY.

THOK

THEY DON'T GIVE US PLUS-ONES.

ZHHH

BESIDES, I DOUBT YOU WOULD'VE CLEARED THE METAL DETECTORS.
GOOD POINT. STILL WOULD'VE BEEN NICE TO HAVE BEEN ASKED.
LEGEND OF THE MANTAMAJI BLOODLINES
CREATED BY ERIC DEAN SEATON
WRITTEN BY ERIC DEAN SEATON AND DAVID ELLIS DICKERSON
ART BY BRANDON PALAS COLORS BY ANDREW DALHOUSE LETTERS BY ANDWORLD DESIGN

CAVALLO IS HERE. HE WAS IN CHARGE OF THE DOCK SHIPMENTS UNDER SIRACH'S STREET REIGN.

HE'S THE MAN WHO KNOWS WHAT WE NEED TO KNOW.

CONTRACTS ALL OVER THE WORLD, WEAPONS, HUMAN TRAFFICKING.

MY OFFICE JUST HASN'T BEEN ABLE TO MAKE ANYTHING STICK.

THAT SUPPORTS MY SUSPICION THAT EVERYTHING WE HAVE FACED SINCE SIRACH* IS CONNECTED.

*SEE LEGEND OF THE MANTAMAJI BOOK 3.

ZHHRSHH

SHHZ

SZZK

BREAKING GLASS.

WE'RE READY.

NO ALARM. WELL DONE, NEWBIE.

MEERKAT'S MY NAME.

THEY CALL ME MEERKAT--

SHE TALKS *TOO MUCH.* LOOP THE SECURITY FEED PLEASE.

YES, DIANA.

GO AHEAD, YOU CAN SAY IT. I'M *GOOD.*

I *WASN'T* GOING TO SAY IT.

I WASN'T EVEN *THINKING* IT.

THE VAULT IS DOWN THE HALL TO YOUR RIGHT.

I'M GOING IN.

DEAR GUESTS, PLEASE TAKE YOUR SEATS.

IT'S STARTING. GOING RADIO SILENT.

IF YOU ARE PAYING IN BITCOIN, PLEASE ONLY USE OUR APPROVED PIRATE SITES.

IF YOU ARE PAYING IN DIAMONDS, HAVE YOUR CERTIFIED APPRAISAL READY FOR INSPECTION. AND IF YOU'RE PAYING IN CASH...

...I HOPE YOU BROUGHT MANY, MANY SUITCASES...

NUMBER 19?

I'M SORRY SIR, BUT, THE CASH AND THE SECRECY, AND THESE ANONYMOUS NUMBERS...

...IS THIS ALL *LEGAL?*

I ASSURE YOU THIS IS ALL LEGAL. THE OFF DUTY POLICE OFFICERS IN ATTENDANCE CAN ATTEST TO THAT.

THE LILY ADAMS INSTITUTE SIMPLY PREFERS TO AVOID PAPER TRAILS AND PROTECT THE ANONYMITY OF OUR PRESTIGIOUS CLIENTELE.

AND NOW FOR OUR FIRST LOT OF THE EVENING. IT'S THE FIRST GREEK COMPUTER, KNOWN AS THE ANTIKYTHERA MECHANISM.

I'M HERE, CORNERSTONE. BUT FOR THE RECORD, I'VE NEVER OPENED A BANK VAULT IN MY LIFE.

YOU WON'T NEED TO. ALL THE ITEMS ARE ON DISPLAY *EXCEPT* FOR WHAT WE WANT. THEY WILL BE HAND DELIVERED TO THE HIGHEST BIDDER AFTER THIS ROUND IS CLOSED.

WHICH BRINGS ME TO MY *SECOND* ISSUE. I TOOK AN OATH TO *UPHOLD THE LAW.* I'M A PROSECUTOR, NOT A *THIEF.*

ALL THESE SALES ARE *PRIVATE.*

WE CAN STILL GET THE PAPERS TO WHOMEVER IS BIDDING ON THEM AFTER WE MAKE SURE THEY DON'T HOLD ANY INFORMATION THAT COULD KICK START THE APOCALYPSE.

HEY, WAIT A MINUTE...

SOMETHING WRONG?

I THOUGHT THE WINDOW WAS BROKEN IN THERE. BUT I GUESS IT WAS JUST THE WAY THE LIGHT REFLECTED ON THE GLASS.

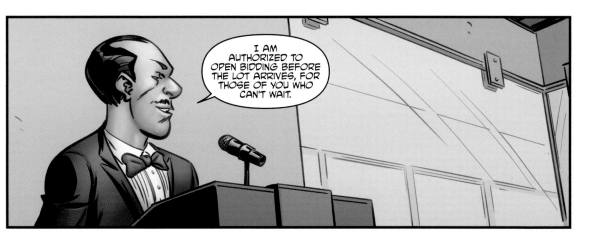

VRRRR

CORNERSTONE, YOU WERE *RIGHT*.

THOSE *ARE* SANCTUANT PAPERS.

THE INSCRIPTION *MATCHES* MY MOTHER'S WORK IN HER "BOOK OF LEGENDS."*

NOAH TOLD ME ABOUT THEM YEARS AGO. SECRET WRITINGS BY OUR *ORIGINAL* MOTHERS. THEY'RE PART OF OUR HISTORY.

THE *SECRET* MAY BE OUT. THERE IS A *BIDDING WAR* GOING ON.

*SEE *LEGEND OF THE MANTAMAJI* BOOK 1.

16

850,000.

900,000.

950,000.

A MILLION.

A MILLION AND ONE.

TWO MILLION.

TWO MILLION AND ONE.

FOUR MILLION.

DO I HEAR FOUR MILLION AND ONE? ANYONE?

I'M ABOUT TO ACQUIRE THEM.

STAND BY.

OKAY, THEN LOT TWO IS *SOLD* TO CLIENT NUMBER 12 FOR *FOUR MILLION DOLLARS.*

NO ONE MUST HAVE THIS! I'LL *DESTROY* IT IF I HAVE TO!

DROP THE GUNS, CAVALLO!

DON'T SHOOT! YOU'LL HURT THE ARTIFACTS!

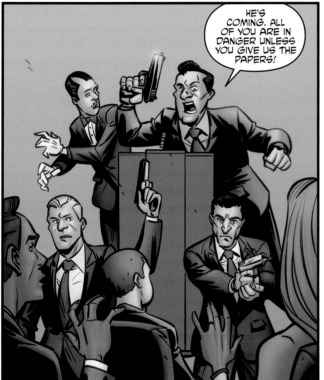

HE'S COMING. ALL OF YOU ARE IN DANGER UNLESS YOU GIVE US THE PAPERS!

WHAT HAPPENED TO THE LIGHTS?

THE BUILDING LOST ITS POWER.

AND WE LOST OUR FEED.

WHERE? THE LIGHTS ARE STILL ON UP HERE.

BLAM
BLAM
BLAM
BLAM

WHO'S SHOOTING?

DING

CAVALLO!

SPREAD OUT!

FWIP

KSHSHSH

KSHASH

ping

spang

KRAK

FREIGHT ELEVATOR IS DOWN TO THE RIGHT!

I CAN'T GET THE LIGHTS BACK ON. IT'S SOME SORT OF ENCRYPTED SIGNAL JAMMER.

THIS HELPS, ACTUALLY.

THWOCK

CHOOM

THWAK

WE HAVE THE PACKAGE AND ARE IN THE ELEVATOR.

MOVE QUICKLY, THINGS HAVE GONE SOUTH UP HERE.

OH...

NOW THAT I SEE IT IN PERSON, DEFINITELY KEEP THE DRESS.

EVERYONE OUT, NOW!

CAVALLO!

DING

WHAM

SIR! WE ARE *UNDER ATTACK!*

THE GARAGE!

BLAM

BY WHOM? WHERE ARE YOU?

CHOOM
CHOOM
CHOOM

DON'T WORRY, SIR! NYPD. COME WITH ME.

GET YOUR HANDS *OFF* ME!

OKAY... WE SHOULD GET YOU OUT OF HERE, RIGHT?

DO YOU STILL HAVE THEM?

WHO ARE YOU TALKING TO, SIR?

LOOKS LIKE YOU'VE GOT TWO CHOICES. JUMP TO YOUR *DEATH*, OR *SURRENDER*.

AHHHH!

STAY AWAY FROM ME!

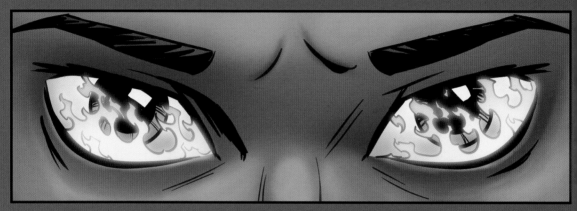

STAY AWAY FROM US ALL!

ZZRAK

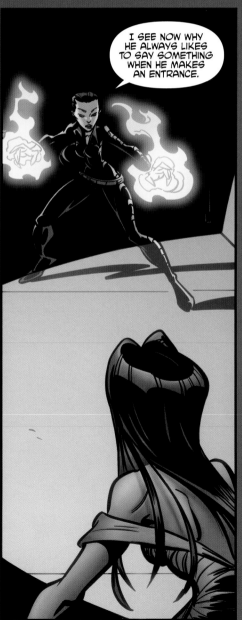

I SEE NOW WHY HE ALWAYS LIKES TO SAY SOMETHING WHEN HE MAKES AN ENTRANCE.

ARE YOU OKAY?

HE'S STRONG. STRONGER THAN A NORMAL MAN.

I DIDN'T PULL ANY PUNCHES. HOW DID HE GET UP FROM THAT?

WHAT'S THAT CARVED INTO THE WALL?

..."ILITYALWE."

ILITYALWE

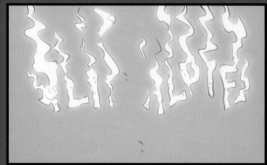

YOU SAW THAT, RIGHT?

WHAT'S IT GONNA BE?

THEY ARE ALL COMING...

...FOR YOU!

KROOM

THAT CRAZY FOOL JUMPED.

TIME TO GO, PEOPLE. COPS ARE STORMING THE BUILDING.

CAN YOU GET US OUT OF HERE?

LET'S GO.

YOU OKAY?

SYDNEY, WHAT'S WRONG?

I RUINED THE DRESS.

CHAPTER ②

My blessed son, the tale, once told, will continue to grow and change. There are things we don't know now that you must learn. And then, you must teach others. A victory is never the end. There will always be a new menace, a new challenge that you must find a new way to defeat.

NEW YORK STATE SUPREME COURT BUILDING, MANHATTAN

THE FACTS ARE THESE: ON THE NIGHT OF THIS MASSIVE SHOOT-OUT AT BROTHER HOPE'S TEMPLE, THERE WERE *DOZENS* OF WITNESSES BEING HELD HOSTAGE BY HOPE'S THUGS.*

AND YET, THROUGHOUT THIS TRIAL, THE DEFENSE HAS SUGGESTED THAT ALL OF THESE EYEWITNESSES, *ALL OF THEM*, ARE "UNRELIABLE."

*SEE LEGEND OF THE MANTAMAJI BOOK 3.

WHY? BECAUSE THEY ALSO SAY THEY SAW *MAGIC BLASTS*, FLAMING SWORDS, GLOWING CRYSTALS, AND SOME KIND OF *TIME-TRAVEL DIMENSIONAL VORTEX*.

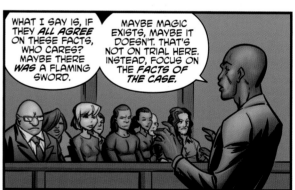

WHAT I SAY IS, IF THEY *ALL AGREE* ON THESE FACTS, WHO CARES? MAYBE THERE *WAS* A FLAMING SWORD.

MAYBE MAGIC EXISTS, MAYBE IT DOESN'T. THAT'S NOT ON TRIAL HERE. INSTEAD, FOCUS ON THE *FACTS OF THE CASE*.

THE DEFENDANT WAS *ON THE SCENE* AT THE TIME OF THE MASS KIDNAPPING, HIS PRINTS WERE ON A GUN USED IN THE INCIDENT, AND *SEVERAL* EYEWITNESSES SAW HIM.

THAT'S ILLEGAL, AND *THAT* SHOULD BE THE *ONLY THING* YOU RETURN JUDGMENT ON. THANK YOU.

DID YOU JUST *HEAR* WHAT THE PROSECUTION JUST SAID? "MAYBE MAGIC EXISTS."

LET THAT *SINK IN* FOR A SECOND.

MAYBE.

MAGIC.

EXISTS.

HE SAYS THAT HIS WITNESSES, WHO CLAIM TO HAVE SEEN MY CLIENT COMMITTING THESE CRIMES, ALSO SAW FLAMING SWORDS AND ENERGY BLASTS AND GLOWING CRYSTALS.

AND YET WE SHOULDN'T QUESTION THEIR TESTIMONY BECAUSE MAYBE THE FLAMING SWORDS ACTUALLY HAPPENED TOO!

IN OTHER WORDS, BY HIS OWN ADMISSION, YOU SHOULD ACCEPT THE EYEWITNESS TESTIMONY, AND MY CLIENT'S GUILT, BECAUSE IT'S JUST AS LIKELY TO BE AS REAL AS THREE THOUSAND YEAR-OLD SORCERERS.

41

CHIEF WOODS, YOU WANTED TO SEE ME?

SPENCER, HAVE A SEAT.

I'M LOOKING OVER THE PAPERWORK FROM LAST NIGHT. WHAT'S MISSING?

I'M NOT SURE I CAN PROVIDE ANY MORE INFORMATION THAN I'VE ALREADY STATED.

THERE HAS BEEN SOMETHING LIKE HALF A DOZEN VIOLENT INCIDENTS INVOLVING THIS *MANTAMAJI* IN THE PAST TWO MONTHS.

AND IN *EVERY CASE* WHERE THE NYPD SHOWED UP, *YOU* WERE *ALREADY THERE*.

THEN LAST NIGHT YOU WERE WORKING PRIVATE SECURITY, THE PLACE GETS ATTACKED,

FELLOW OFFICERS WORKING SECURITY WERE BEATEN UP, AND GUESS WHO'S LEFT *UNHARMED*. ARE YOU SAYING THIS IS A *COINCIDENCE?*

I BELIEVE THE VIGILANTE WAS TRYING TO HELP.

AND, RIGHT OR WRONG, THE OTHER OFFICERS ATTACKED HIM FIRST.

DOES THAT GIVE HIM *THE RIGHT* TO THROW A GANGSTER OUT OF A WINDOW?

YOU CAN TELL THE DIFFERENCE BETWEEN SOMEONE WHO JUMPS AND SOMEONE WHO'S BEEN THROWN. THERE'S NO PROOF THAT HE DID THE LATTER.

I DID MY HOMEWORK ON YOU. THEY USED TO CALL YOU *SUPERNATURAL SPENCER.*

YOU GOT A LOT OF CRITICISM FROM YOUR FELLOW COPS WHEN YOU WERE ON THIS ONE-WOMAN CRUSADE AGAINST *THE NEW WORLD KNIGHTS*, WHICH YOU CLAIMED...

HOLD ON....

...YOU CLAIMED THEY WERE "CRIMINALS PROTECTED FROM THE LAW BY MYSTICAL POWERS OF DISGUISE AND OBFUSCATION." EVERYONE MADE FUN OF YOU.

FORMER COMMANDER COTTON* EVEN LET YOU WORK *WITHOUT A PARTNER* BECAUSE-- ACCORDING TO HIS NOTES--NO ONE WANTED TO WORK WITH YOU.

COTTON* WAS NOT A GOOD MAN, CHIEF.

*SEE LEGEND OF THE MANTAMAJI BOOK 2 & 3.

BUT WHEN I LOOK OVER THIS HISTORY, HERE'S WHAT I SEE. YOU WERE *RIGHT.* THE NEW WORLD KNIGHTS *DID EXIST.*

AND EYEWITNESSES CLAIM TO HAVE SEEN THINGS THAT... WELL, THAT WE DON'T HAVE A LOT OF EXPLANATIONS FOR.

BLASTS OF POWER, ILLUSIONS, PORTALS, YOU MIGHT CALL IT... *MAGIC.*

THESE ARE THINGS THAT ARE HARD TO EXPLAIN, CHIEF. BUT I'M A *GOOD* DETECTIVE. I FOLLOW THE *LAW.*

WHAT ABOUT THESE *WOMEN* THE MANTAMAJI WORKS WITH? WOMEN WHO...

...SHOOT BLASTS OF ENERGY FROM THEIR *HANDS?*

THAT'S FROM AN EYEWITNESS WHO HASN'T WAVERED IN THEIR STORY AFTER *FOUR* DEPOSITIONS.

MAYBE THIS WORLD IS *BIGGER AND MORE UNEXPLAINABLE* THAN SCIENCE HAS LED US TO BELIEVE.

MANHATTAN, NEW YORK
DISTRICT ATTORNEY'S OFFICE

WHAT'S GOING ON?

D.A. PHILLIPS IS BACK.

ALEXANDER!

WELCOME BACK, SIR.

MY OFFICE, NOW!

I WAS HOPING TO TALK TO YOU. I'VE GOT SOME IDEAS FOR THE NEXT DEFENDANT. HE'S GOT A PRIOR FOR--

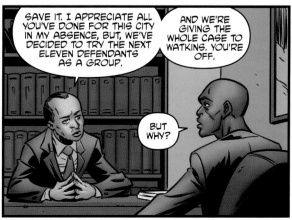

SAVE IT. I APPRECIATE ALL YOU'VE DONE FOR THIS CITY IN MY ABSENCE, BUT, WE'VE DECIDED TO TRY THE NEXT ELEVEN DEFENDANTS AS A GROUP.

AND WE'RE GIVING THE WHOLE CASE TO WATKINS. YOU'RE OFF.

BUT WHY?

THIS IS *FIVE IN A ROW* YOU'VE LOST, AND I DON'T SEE A GOOD STRATEGY HERE. WE NEED FRESH EYES.

BOSS, THE NEXT CASE IS DICKERSON. IT'S *OPEN-AND-SHUT!*

LOOK, ELIJAH, WE ALL HAVE BAD MONTHS. THIS DOESN'T WRECK YOUR CAREER. IT'S JUST A SETBACK. SO, TAKE A BACK SEAT FOR A WHILE AND LET EVERYTHING COOL DOWN.

WE HAVE *A SIGNED CONFESSION!* HE *SHOWED* US HIS GUN. WE GOT *FINGERPRINTS.* WE *KNOW* HE WAS THERE.

THE ONLY QUESTIONS ARE WHETHER OR NOT HE'LL ROLL ON HIS FELLOW GANGSTERS, AND HOW LONG THE SENTENCE WILL BE. BUT HE'S *100% GUILTY,* GUARANTEED PROVABLE.

OKAY. BUT IF YOU SCREW UP, GETTING BACK ON TOP MAY NOT BE AN OPTION.

UNDERSTOOD. THANK YOU, SIR.

IN THE MEANTIME, I JUST HAVE ONE WORD OF ADVICE...

UNLESS YOU CAN PROVE IT'S REAL, I *NEVER* WANT TO HEAR THE WORD *"MAGIC"* IN MY COURTHOUSE EVER AGAIN. IS THAT CLEAR?

CRYSTAL.

POLICE ARE NOT CONFIRMING THE MANTAMAJI'S APPEARANCE, BUT IF IT TURNS OUT TO BE TRUE, THIS WOULD BE THE *SIXTH* SIGHTING OF THE MANTAMAJI SINCE THE GLOBAL TERRORIST EVENT AT HOPE'S TEMPLE TWO MONTHS AGO.

IN OTHER NEWS, A FAMILY WAS BRUTALLY *MURDERED* IN BROOKLYN HEIGHTS LAST NIGHT.

I COME TO BEAR WITNESS TO THE TRUTH.

SWOOSH

HAVEN HOTEL

NOK
NOK

AND I THOUGHT *I* DIDN'T GET ANY SLEEP LAST NIGHT.

BEFORE NOAH BECAME A SERVANT* TO SIRACH, HE USED TO HAVE MY MOTHER KEEP TABS ON OTHER POSSIBLE THREATS TO HUMANITY

*SEE LEGEND OF THE MANTAMAJI BOOK 3.

APPARENTLY THEY WEREN'T ALWAYS TRYING TO ELIMINATE SIRACH'S NEW WORLD KNIGHTS.

BUT ONCE SIRACH WAS RESURRECTED,* SURVIVAL BECAME PRIORITY NUMBER ONE, AND ALL OF THIS FELL BY THE WAYSIDE.

*SEE LEGEND OF THE MANTAMAJI BOOK 1.

EVERYTHING WE HAVE FACED SINCE WE DEFEATED SIRACH IS BASED OFF INFO FROM THESE FILES.

IF MY MOTHER HAD HAD A DYING WISH, IT WOULD HAVE BEEN TO COMPARE THESE FILES OF HERS WITH THE ANCIENT WRITINGS.

ANYTHING USEFUL YET?

THE WORD *"ILITYALWE"* YOUR ATTACKER LEFT ON THE WALL MEANS--

"FORGOTTEN." IN XHOSA, A SOUTH AFRICAN LANGUAGE. I LOOKED UP TRANSLATION ENGINES ONLINE.

IT TOOK *MAYBE* TEN MINUTES. MIGHT HAVE GONE FASTER, BUT XHOSA IS *REALLY* FAR BACK IN THE ALPHABET...

YOUR ANCIENT FILES DIDN'T TELL YOU THAT?

NO, BUT IT'S INTERESTING YOU SAY THAT THE WORD MEANS "FORGOTTEN." LOOK HERE.

THESE ARE SACRED STORIES, GOING BACK ALMOST THREE THOUSAND YEARS. AND LOOK AT THIS...

...First before all things, the Enlightened Ones came to change mankind...

"...FIRST BEFORE ALL THINGS, THE ENLIGHTENED ONES CAME TO CHANGE MANKIND..."

THAT'S THE FAMOUS FIRST LINE OF OUR STORY. BUT LOOK HERE...

THERE WAS SOMETHING THAT CAME *BEFORE THE BEGINNING.* PAGES HAVE BEEN *REMOVED.*

HOW MANY *MORE* PAGES ARE LIKE THIS?

SO FAR, TWENTY.

DID YOU FIND *THAT* ON YOUR COMPUTER?

STOP SMILING. IT'S WEIRD.

THERE'S *MORE.*

REMIND ME, WHAT DID THE MAN WHO TRIED TO KILL YOU LAST NIGHT LOOK LIKE ?

53

WELL, HE WAS ABOUT...FIVE...NO...*SIX*...WHAT WAS--

ILITYALWE WASN'T JUST A *WORD*. IT WAS A *SPELL*. WE HAVE FORGOTTEN HIM.

WHOA.

EXACTLY.

I NEED TO GET ALL THIS DIGITIZED.

MAKE YOURSELF AT HOME.

ELIJAH

Hey, it's me. I'm at the Hotel. Where are you?

...ONLY THE LATEST IN A SERIES OF DEFEATS FOR ADA ELIJAH ALEXANDER...

BARTENDER? GET ANOTHER ONE FOR MY FRIEND HERE. MY TREAT.

GUTIERREZ. GOOD WORK TODAY. YOU CAN GO NOW.

WHY WOULD I LEAVE WHEN I CAN SEE YOU *LIKE THIS?*

WE SHOULDN'T BE TALKING.

OF COURSE WE CAN TALK. AFTER THE DICKERSON TRIAL, YOU'RE BEING SHELVED. EVERYONE'S TALKING ABOUT IT.

MUST BE SO *EMBARRASSING,* THE YOUNG HOTSHOT LAWYER BEING MOCKED IN PUBLIC.

HURTS, DOESN'T IT?

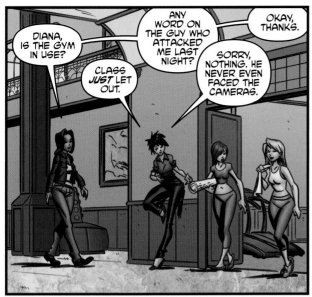

DIANA, IS THE GYM IN USE?

CLASS *JUST* LET OUT.

ANY WORD ON THE GUY WHO ATTACKED ME LAST NIGHT?

SORRY, NOTHING. HE NEVER EVEN FACED THE CAMERAS.

OKAY, THANKS.

NO MATTER HOW LONG YOU HANG LIKE THAT YOU'RE NOT GOING TO GET ANY TALLER.

HA HA. VERY FUNNY.

I'M HANGING LIKE THIS BECAUSE BLOOD FLOW IS *GOOD* FOR THE BRAIN.

I HAVE A THEORY THAT THE INCREASED BRAIN FLOW MAY ALLOW US TO EXPAND OUR MAGIC ABILITIES TO THEIR ORIGINAL FORM, ALLOWING US TO DO MORE THAN JUST SEND BIOGENIC BLASTS OF ENERGY.

IS IT WORKING?

NOT YET. SO, ARE YOU AND ELIJAH SERIOUS? THE WAY HE LOOKS AT YOU IS SO ROMANTIC! ARE YOU GUYS GONNA GET MARRIED?

WE HAVEN'T REALLY...

WHY NOT? YOU TWO WOULD HAVE THE MOST GORGEOUS BABY. HOPEFULLY, IT WILL GET YOUR HEAD. HIS IS KIND OF LARGE FOR A MAN HIS SIZE. DO YOU THINK THAT CAN BE MEDICALLY ENHANCED?

MEERKAT! PLEASE.

I'M DOING IT AGAIN, HUH? SORRY. IT'S JUST THAT NOW THAT WE ARE FULFILLING OUR ORIGINAL SANCTUARY DECREE TO PROTECT THE WORLD FROM THE FORCES OF EVIL, EVERYTHING FEELS SO SPECIAL, SO IMPORTANT.

OUR MOTHERS WOULD BE PROUD THAT THEIR SACRIFICE TO RAISE ELIJAH AND HIS MOTHER WAS NOT IN VAIN. I JUST DON'T WANT TO MISS ANYTHING.

THEN MAKE SURE YOU LISTEN AS MUCH AS YOU CAN.

SORRY, I WASN'T LISTENING....KIDDING. I GET WHERE YOU'RE GOING. I CAN DO THAT.

MEERKAT, THERE YOU ARE. I NEED YOU TO HELP ME DIGITIZE SOMETHING.

58

THOOM

FWSHH

FWOOM

FROM LEGEND OF THE MANTAMAJI BOOK 3.

UNNH!!

AHH!

UGH!

BAM

BAM

BAM

WHAT'S GOING ON?

MY BAD.

SYD?

IT'S OKAY. I GOT IT.

WHAT DID THAT DUMMY DO TO HER?

QUIET.

SYD, THIS IS A *TRAINING* ROOM, NOT A *GUN RANGE!*

I *KNOW.* SORRY.

WHAT'S ALL THIS ABOUT?

I JUST WANT TO BE ABLE TO DO WHAT I *SHOULD* BE DOING.

LOOKS LIKE YOU ARE.

LAST NIGHT, MY GUN WASN'T ENOUGH.

YOU'RE THE ONLY SANCTUANT WHOSE POWERS EMERGED IN LATER LIFE. MOST OF US KNOW WHO WE ARE FROM CHILDHOOD. WE DON'T KNOW WHAT THIS MEANS FOR YOU. OUR OTHER RULES MAY NOT APPLY EITHER.

I'M THE ONLY LATE BLOOMER SANCTUANT IN *THOUSANDS* OF YEARS? COME ON. DON'T YOU HAVE ANY STORIES PASSED DOWN ABOUT SANCTUANTS WHO GAINED THEIR ABILITIES UNDER STRESS, IN THE HEAT OF A DANGEROUS MOMENT?

NOT THAT I KNOW OF.

WHAT HAPPENS THE *NEXT* TIME YOU'RE NOT THERE TO SAVE ME?

WE JUST NEED TO BE MORE CAREFUL.

IT HAS ONLY BEEN TWO MONTHS AND EVERYTHING WE HAVE FACED HAS BEEN *BEYOND* NORMAL POLICE WORK. UNTIL I CAN GET A HANDLE ON THINGS, MAYBE IT'S TIME I STEPPED BACK.

I'VE NEVER SEEN YOU AFRAID OF ANYTHING OR ANYONE. WHAT'S *THIS* ABOUT?

MY *MORTALITY*. LAST NIGHT, ELIJAH LEFT THE MISSION BECAUSE HE WAS WORRIED ABOUT ME. IF I'D HAD MY POWERS, HE WOULDN'T HAVE HAD TO.

HE LEFT THE MISSION BECAUSE HE LOVES YOU. AND I FOR ONE THINK HE MADE THE *RIGHT* CALL.

SAYS THE *IMMORTAL*.

WE DON'T AGE LIKE HUMANS, BUT WE'RE *NOT* IMMORTAL. WE HAVE ALWAYS DIED FIGHTING TO SAVE MANKIND.

THEN THERE'S *THAT.* YOU ALL STAY YOUNG FOREVER, AND EVENTUALLY I'LL BE... *FORGOTTEN.*

OUR POWERS COME FROM OUR MINDS. AND YOURS SEEMS TO BE TO FOCUSED IN THE *WRONG PLACE.*

WHY DON'T YOU TAKE LEAVE FROM BEING A DETECTIVE AND COME TRAIN WITH US FULL TIME?

YOU THINK IT WILL MAKE A DIFFERENCE?

THERE ARE NO GUARANTEES. THE ONLY THING I KNOW FOR SURE IS, YOU NEED TO MAKE *PEACE* WITH *WHO* YOU ARE, NOT WORRY ABOUT *WHAT* YOU ARE.

HOW DID YOU DO IT, MOM?

HOW DID YOU HOLD DOWN JOBS, RAISE ME AS A SINGLE MOM, AND STILL KEEP YOUR SANCTUANT ABILITIES A SECRET?

MARIAH ALEXANDER

YOU HAD MY ENTIRE HEART MY ENTIRE LIFE

SHE LIVED AN ETERNITY BELIEVING IN LIFE FOR ALL

DID YOU EVER GET TIRED OF HIDING WHO YOU WERE?

NEVER THOUGHT AS AN ADULT I'D MISS OUR STORY TIME AS MUCH AS I DO.

NORTH DAKOTA, CHRISTMAS EVE, 24 YEARS AGO.

ELIJAH, COME AWAY FROM THAT WINDOW. IT'S COLD.

WHY DO THEY GET PRESENTS AND WE DON'T?

I'M SORRY, ELIJAH. IT HAS BEEN ANOTHER HARD YEAR. MAYBE IF WE MOVE AGAIN...

HEY, ELIJAH! REMEMBER HOW THERE ARE MORE IMPORTANT THINGS THAN PRESENTS?

YEAH...

WELL, I HAVE A SURPRISE FOR YOU.

I MADE IT MYSELF.

IS THAT MINE?

YES.

FOREVER.

WHAT'S THE STORY?

STORIES. THESE ARE TALES OF LEGENDS. DO YOU WANT TO HEAR ONE?

YES!!!

COME HERE.

MY NOBLE SON, I MUST TELL YOU ABOUT AN ANCIENT TALE...

...A DARK TALE OF MONSTERS AND MAGIC, VILLAINS AND HEROES WITH NAMES YOU DO NOT KNOW, BUT WHOSE STORY ECHOES EVEN TODAY...

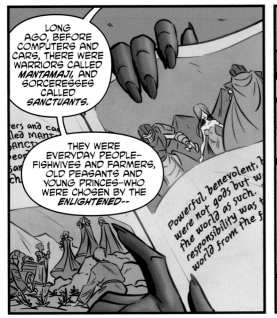

LONG AGO, BEFORE COMPUTERS AND CARS, THERE WERE WARRIORS CALLED *MANTAMAJI*, AND SORCERESSES CALLED *SANCTUANTS*.

THEY WERE EVERYDAY PEOPLE—FISHWIVES AND FARMERS, OLD PEASANTS AND YOUNG PRINCES—WHO WERE CHOSEN BY THE *ENLIGHTENED*—

—POWERFUL, BENEVOLENT, BEINGS WHO WERE NOT GODS BUT WATCHED OVER THE WORLD AS SUCH. THE MANTAMAJI'S RESPONSIBILITY WAS TO DEFEND THE WORLD FROM THE FORCES OF EVIL.

NO MATTER WHAT THE CHALLENGE WAS, THE MANTAMAJI WERE UNSTOPPABLE, INESCAPABLE AND DEVASTATED THEIR FOES BEFORE VANISHING AGAIN WITH THE AID OF A MYSTICAL ORB USED FOR TRAVEL. THEIR MISSION ALWAYS CAME BEFORE THEMSELVES.

SO, I KNOW WE DON'T HAVE A LOT OF MATERIAL THINGS, BUT REMEMBER, IT'S WHAT WE DO WITH WHAT WE HAVE THAT DEFINES WHO WE ARE.

NOW THIS NEXT STORY I WILL TELL YOU TOMORROW NIGHT, IS HOW THE SANCTUANTS LEARNED THAT THE GREATEST WEALTH OF ALL IS HAVING A PURPOSE...

I HEAR YOU, MOM.

I MISS YOU.

WHO'S THERE?

EVEN AS *LOVE* CROWNS YOU, SO SHALL HE *CRUCIFY* YOU.

WHAT? WHO'S *THAT?*

ARF ARF ARF

LISTEN, MISTER, I DON'T KNOW...

EVEN AS HE IS FOR YOUR *GROWTH*, SO IS HE FOR YOUR *PRUNING.*

NO, IT CAN'T BE.

EVEN AS HE IS FORGOTTEN, HE REMEMBERED HIS PEOPLE AND *CAME FOR THEM.*

DARKNESS.

KZKK

ARF ARF ARF

YOU CAN'T COME IN!

NOT UNLESS YOU *INVITE* HIM.

PLEASE COME IN.

WHOOSH

ARF

ARF

ARF

TIME WOULD NOT LET YOU NEGLECT THE GIFT THAT IS IN YOU, WHICH WAS *GIVEN TO YOU* THROUGH PROPHECY.

ARF
ARF
ARF
ARF

SHHHH.

AR--

THANK YOU.

YOU HAVE LIVED IN *PLEASURE* ON THE EARTH. FAT, COMFORTABLE, AFRAID. TELL ME WHERE IT IS.

I DON'T KNOW.

YOU FELT SAFE ENOUGH TO LIVE AMONG THE HUMANS. YOU MUST HAVE AN *IDEA*.

I DON'T, GIDEON. I *SWEAR*.

FORTUNATELY FOR YOU, I CAN'T BE LIED TO.

UNFORTUNATELY FOR YOU, YOU HAVE *BETRAYED* YOUR BROTHERS AND SISTERS.

COME IN, CHILDREN.

BROTHER NUBAN, SISTER TEL.

TO BE CONTINUED...

CHAPTER ③

The Mantamaji do not fear darkness, for they bring their own light wherever they go. This is why the darkness hates them, hungers for them. The darkness will get in whenever it can.

SECURITY AROUND THE J.F.K. AIRPORT HAS BEEN DOUBLED WITH THE ANTICIPATED ARRIVAL OF PRESIDENT AMUN KESH, THE LEADER OF AL'LA-MAKAN.

THIS MARKS AMUN KESH'S FIRST VISIT TO THE UNITED STATES.

A RECEPTION IN HIS HONOR WILL BE HELD TOMORROW AT THE ST. REGIS HOTEL.

THERE YOU ARE. HOW ARE YOU DOING?

HAVEN'T YOU SEEN THE NEWS?

COME HERE, WARRIOR.

HOW ARE WE SUPPOSED TO DO OUR JOBS?

THESE PEOPLE ARE GUILTY AND WE CAN'T PROVE IT WITHOUT REVEALING WHO WE REALLY ARE.

I FEEL LIKE THIS IS CHIPPING AWAY AT MY SOUL.

WE HAVE BEEN PUT HERE WITH THESE GIFTS TO EFFECT CHANGE AND TRULY MAKE A DIFFERENCE.

EVEN *WITH* POWERS, LIFE IS NO DIFFERENT THAN THE STRUGGLE PEOPLE FACE EVERY DAY.

GROWING UP, I THOUGHT BECOMING SUCCESSFUL AND POWERFUL WAS THE ANSWER TO EVERYTHING.

AND THEN I LEARNED THE TRUTH ABOUT MY PAST. ABOUT YOU. ABOUT OUR POWERS.

NOW I JUST WANT TO HELP DO MY PART. BUT THE WORLD IS NOT MAKING IT EASY.

DID YOU THINK IT WOULD BE?

I DIDN'T ENVISION OUR *DAY JOBS* WOULD BE THE ISSUE.

WE HAVE TO FIND THAT *BALANCE* BETWEEN BOTH WORLDS, WHICH IS WHY FOR ME, I MAY HAVE TO TAKE A STEP BACK.

HOW WOULD THAT EVEN THE SCALE?

I'M A DETECTIVE RUNNING AROUND WITH SUPER BEINGS--

YOU'RE A *SANCTUANT.*

NO, I'M *NOT.* AND THERE IS NO GUARANTEE I EVER *WILL* BE.

IT'S WHAT I BELIEVE.

80

...*BELIEVE.* GOT IT. MAN, I WISH I HAD YOUR OPTIMISM. BUT RIGHT NOW, WE HAVE TO PLAY IT SMART.

AS LONG AS I'M NOT FULLY LIKE YOU, I'M PUTTING *EVERYONE* IN DANGER.

FIRST OF ALL, WE DEFEATED SIRACH* *TOGETHER* AND THAT'S HOW WE ARE GOING TO REMAIN NO MATTER WHAT HAPPENS. SECOND--

DING DONG

*SEE LEGEND OF THE MANTAMAJI BOOK 3.

ELIJAH ALEXANDER?

WHO WANTS TO KNOW?

YOUR PRESENCE IS REQUESTED AT THE *AL'LA-MAKAN RECEPTION* TOMORROW NIGHT AT *THE ROYAL EMBASSY.*

THANK YOU.

AL'LA-MAKAN? THAT LITTLE AFRICAN COUNTRY WITH ALL THE *TECH METALS?*

HOW DID YOU GET AN INVITATION TO *THAT?*

I'M SORT OF... FRIENDS WITH THE PRINCESS.

PRINCESS YOLA KESH? *"THE AFRICAN AMIDALA?"*

THE *WHO?*

SHE PULLED A *PADME* A FEW YEARS BACK-- ATTENDED SOUTH BY SOUTHWEST WITH *SIX LOOKALIKES,* AND NO ONE KNEW WHICH ONE WAS HER.

IT WAS A *SCANDAL* FOR HER TO BE SEEN IN PUBLIC. APPARENTLY DADDY WAS FURIOUS.

I MISSED THAT STORY. MUST HAVE HAPPENED DURING LAW SCHOOL. BUT THAT SOUNDS LIKE THEIR RELATIONSHIP.

WE MET IN HIGH SCHOOL. SHE WAS AN EXCHANGE STUDENT UNTIL HER FATHER FORCED HER TO COME HOME.

WE LOST TOUCH AFTER THAT.

WELL IT SEEMS SHE KEPT TABS ON YOU.

You and a guest are invited to an informal dinner with President Amun Kesh and his daughter, Yola, at the Al la-Mak Embassy, Sat, 8pm.

NOT HARD TO DO WHEN I'M IN THE NEWS EVERYDAY.

WAIT, WHERE ARE YOU GOING?

A *BILLIONAIRE PRINCESS* FROM ANOTHER COUNTRY JUST HAD ONE OF HER SERVANTS DELIVER A PERSONALIZED INVITATION FOR YOU AND A GUEST TO ATTEND THEIR COMING OUT PARTY.

I NEED A DRESS.

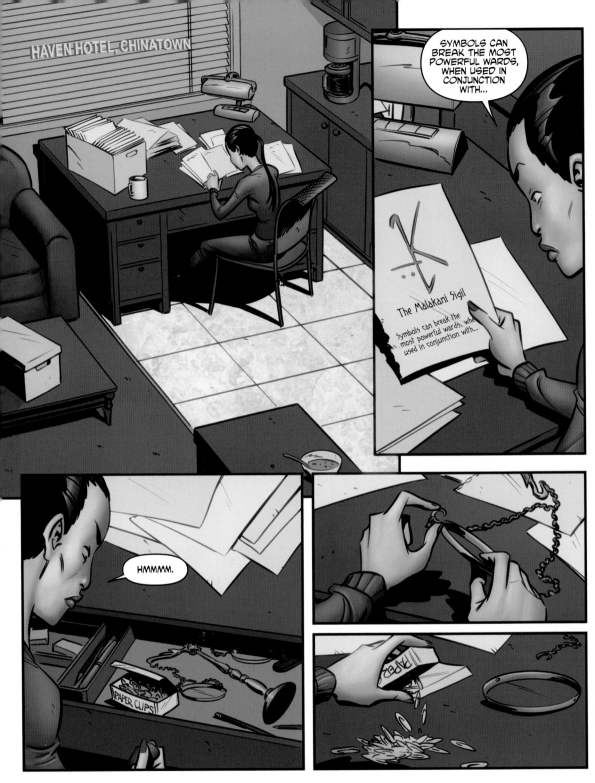

WHOOSH

SISTER! IS EVERYTHING OKAY IN THERE?

"EVERYTHING'S FINE."

ROCHESTER, NEW YORK

PLEASE, GIDEON! WE DON'T KNOW WHERE IT IS! YOU *HAVE* TO BELIEVE US!

NO ONE WHO PUTS A HAND TO THE PLOW AND LOOKS BACK IS FIT FOR SERVICE IN MY KINGDOM.

DID YOU FEEL THAT?

NO, HOW COULD YOU?

I GAVE YOU THE POWER TO TREAD UPON SERPENTS AND SCORPIONS AND THE FULL FORCE OF THE ENEMY, YET YOU THREW IT AWAY TO BE HUMAN.

AAAHHH!!

A DEEP MAGIC HAS BEEN UNLEASHED...

OLD BROCKVILLE, NEW YORK

IT'S ADAM. I'M SORRY I HAVEN'T CALLED. I...LOST THE PAPERS.

YES, WELL, YOU INSISTED I BID ON THEM.

NO, I *DID NOT* CALL YOU TO PLACE BLAME. I JUST WANTED YOU TO KNOW.

"IT APPEARS SOMEONE HAS ACCESSED THE SECRET THAT COULD GET US ALL *KILLED.*"

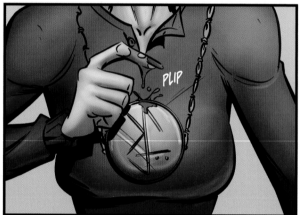

PLIP

KSHHH

...THE FIRST-EVER OFFICIAL PUBLIC APPEARANCE OF PRESIDENT *AMUN KESH* AND HIS DAUGHTER *YOLA.*

AL'LA-MAKAN IS A DEEPLY *SECRETIVE* COUNTRY WHOSE PEOPLE ALMOST NEVER LEAVE THE BORDERS OF THE STATE, AND FOR DECADES IT WAS EVEN *ILLEGAL* TO TAKE PHOTOS OF ANY MEMBER OF THE ROYAL FAMILY--THE SAME ROYAL FAMILY WHO, SINCE 1998, HAVE BEEN THE ELECTED GOVERNMENT OF THE COUNTRY.

YOU READY?

I THINK THE QUESTION SHOULD BE...

...ARE YOU?

KESH SAID HE'S WILLING TO SIT DOWN WITH THE RESISTANCE'S LEADERS, BUT THAT THEY HAVE REJECTED NEGOTIATIONS.

SINCE AL'LA-MAKAN IS ONE OF THE MOST *SECRETIVE* COUNTRIES IN THE WORLD... IT'S HARD TO DETERMINE THE TRUTH.

DID YOU EVER MEET THE KING?

HE'S THE *PRESIDENT.*

RUMOR SAYS THAT'S JUST A TITLE. I MEAN, *COME ON.* THEY HAVE THEIR FIRST DEMOCRATIC ELECTION IN 1998 AND JUST RE-ELECT THEIR OWN MONARCHS.

THIS IS *AMAZING.*

"THE STYLE..."

"...THE MUSIC..."

"...THE PEOPLE..."

...EVERYTHING HERE IS SO *BEAUTIFUL.*

IT REALLY IS.

WE *HAVE* TO TRY THE FOOD.

YOLA.

OH! DID THEY NAME A DISH AFTER HIS DAUGHTER?

YOUR LIPS ARE JUST AS I REMEMBER THEM.

EXCUSE ME?

YOLA KESH, THIS IS SYDNEY, SYDNEY SPENCER.

HIS *GIRLFRIEND.*

OH, I'M SO SORRY, PLEASE FORGIVE ME. I WAS JUST SO *HAPPY* TO SEE HIM.

IT'S OKAY.

IS IT *REALLY?*

I MEAN YOU NO HARM. IT WAS *SILLY* OF ME TO THINK ELIJAH WOULD NOT HAVE MOVED ON.

MOVED ON? I DIDN'T KNOW HE MADE A STOP.

WE WERE *KIDS.*

HE WAS MY FIRST KISS. HOW LONG HAS IT BEEN?

FIFTEEN YEARS.

AND YET I *STILL* REMEMBER IT!

BEHIND THE BLEACHERS, AFTER CHEERLEADING PRACTICE. IT WAS RAINING--

IT WAS *SNOWING.*

WAS IT? YOU ALWAYS HAD THE BEST MEMORY.

REALLY? BECAUSE HE *FORGOT* TO TELL *ME* ALL ABOUT THE TWO OF YOU.

YOU'LL HAVE TO EXCUSE ME. IT IS SO GREAT TO SEE YOU, ELIJAH!

AND YOU TOO...*MISS.*

IT'S SPENCER. *DETECTIVE* SPENCER, NYPD.

LET ME EXPLAIN.

I'M NOT STOPPING YOU.

97

WELL, WELL. I GUESS *ANYONE* CAN GET A TICKET TO THIS THING.

I GUESS SO.

I HOPE YOU'RE NOT THAT BAD WITH THE *COMEBACKS* IN COURT TOMORROW. THEN AGAIN, *MAYBE I DO.*

WHAT DO YOU WANT, GUTIERREZ?

OH, DON'T GET MAD, DETECTIVE. I WAS JUST SAYING HELLO.

LADIES AND GENTLEMEN...PLEASE WELCOME, PRINCESS YOLA KESH.

OH, HOLD THAT THOUGHT. THE SHOW IS ABOUT TO BEGIN.

PLEASE CRUSH HIM TOMORROW.

I *PLAN* TO.

GOOD EVENING, EVERYONE. TONIGHT I HAVE THE *PLEASURE* OF INTRODUCING A MAN MOST OF YOU HAVE HEARD ABOUT BUT FEW, UNTIL NOW, HAVE EVER SEEN.

CLAP

CLAP

CLAP

CLAP

CLAP

CLAP

CLAP

OUR COUNTRY LIKES ITS PRIVACY AND ITS TRADITIONAL WAYS. BUT WE LIVE IN A *GLOBAL VILLAGE,* AND ISOLATIONISM IS *NO LONGER PRACTICAL.*

WE HAVE COME TO AMERICA AS OUR FIRST STEP ONTO THE WORLD STAGE...

CLAP

CLAP

CLAP

YOU'RE STARING.

IT'S WEIRD TO SEE SOMEONE YOU KNEW IN HIGH SCHOOL TURN INTO A...*POLITICIAN.* A HEAD OF STATE.

ESPECIALLY AFTER YOU'VE SEEN THEM *NAKED.*

IT WAS JUST A *KISS!* I SWEAR.

A *FEW* KISSES.

LADIES AND GENTLEMEN, PLEASE WELCOME MY FATHER, *PRESIDENT AMUN KESH.*

CLAP CLAP CLAP CLAP CLAP CLAP

CLAP CLAP CLAP CLAP CLAP

BROTHERS AND SISTERS. IT IS AN *HONOR* TO BE HERE TONIGHT.

MY DAUGHTER AND I HAVE CROSSED THE ATLANTIC TO COME TO THIS GREAT LAND SO WE CAN CREATE A *PLATFORM* TO RECOGNIZE WHAT WE *ARE* AND WHAT WE WANT TO *BE* IN THIS WORLD.

MY GOD!

ACK!

BRATATAT

RUN!

BRATATATATAT

BRATATAT

<QUIET! ALL OF YOU!>

DON'T.

<HELLO KESH>

SLAMM

FWOOM

FWOOM

GET YOUR HANDS OFF MY FATHER...

...NOW!

I KNOW WHAT YOU *ARE*, WOMAN. HE'LL BE *DEAD* BEFORE YOU CAN UNLEASH YOUR HELL.

ZZZHU

YOLA, *DON'T!*

SYD, HER HANDS.

WHAT IS HAPPENING? WHAT IS SHE?

GO AHEAD. LET'S SEE IF YOUR WORDS ARE FASTER THAN A *BULLET.*

PLEASE, YOLA. REMAIN CALM.

ALA-....

FATHER....

THOK

GOOD THINKING. YOU BOTH MIGHT SURVIVE THIS, PRESIDENT.

WHAT IS IT YOU WANT?

WE KNOW THIS ISN'T A *DIPLOMATIC MISSION.*

YOU'RE HERE TO MEET OUR OLD ENEMY AND *BETRAY* OUR PEOPLE. WE CAN'T LET THAT HAPPEN.

ELIJAH, WHAT ARE YOU DOING?

WHAT I CAN.

THEY CAN'T SEE ME.

AN ILLUSION HERE? NO WAY!

WE ARE THE *GUARDIANS OF FAITH*, AND WE'RE HERE TO EXPOSE THE TRUTH ABOUT THIS TYRANT! THE LIES, THE SUPPRESSION, THE TORTURE.

IT'S TOO DANGEROUS.

WE HAVE TO DO *SOMETHING.*

SOMEONE IN HERE MIGHT PANIC AND BLOW THE ILLUSION.

I CAN KEEP A HANDLE ON IT.

JUST GET AS MANY PEOPLE AS CLOSE TO THE DOORS AS YOU CAN.

HIS ELECTION IN 1998 WAS A *SHAM.* AL'LA-MAKAN IS STILL A MONARCHY. A *DICTATORSHIP,* AND HE IS HERE TO *STRENGTHEN HIS POWER.*

FOLLOW ME.

I CAN'T EXPLAIN THIS RIGHT NOW AND EVEN IF I COULD IT MIGHT NOT MAKE SENSE.

BUT IF YOU WANT TO LIVE, YOU WILL DO *EXACTLY* WHAT I SAY.

NOW QUIETLY AND QUICKLY, GET UP AND FOLLOW ME TO THE DOOR.

FOR YEARS HE COMMITTED *CRIMES* AGAINST HIS PEOPLE. CRIMES HE *MUST* ANSWER FOR.

WHAT IS HAPPENING?

SHHHH.

STAY LOW AND DON'T OPEN THAT DOOR UNTIL I TELL YOU.

THAT IS *NOT TRUE.* EVERYTHING I HAVE DONE HAS BEEN FOR OUR PEOPLE.

DO YOU HEAR *THIS?* DO YOU HEAR *THESE* LIES!

BRING A MAN TO HIS KNEES AND THE TRUTH WILL FLOW DOWN LIKE A STREAM.

I NEED HELP.

IT'S OKAY, TRUST HER.

SEE?

YOU SHOULD NEVER HAVE LEFT OUR HOME COUNTRY. NOW WE CAN GET AT YOU-- *TRAITOR!*

EXPOSE YOUR SECRETS FOR ALL TO SEE.

THERE YOU GO, SEE. KEEP COMING.

YOU CAN'T DO THAT. PEOPLE WON'T UNDERSTAND. THEY WILL TRY TO EXPLOIT OUR EXISTENCE.

LIKE YOU HAVE EXPLOITED YOUR POSITION?

THE PEOPLE HAVE TOLERATED YOU.

YOU WANT TO REUNITE WITH OUR ENEMY TO CREATE SOMETHING TERRIBLE.

NO YOU HAVE IT ALL WRONG.

CHINATOWN

I'VE NOW TRACKED DOWN THE SIGIL THAT APPEARED LAST NIGHT. IT'S IN AN OLD HOTEL. LOOKS LIKE A TOUGH PLACE.

GUARDED.

WARDED. I'LL—

VRRRMM

VRRRRAMM

WAIT.

DON'T YOU SEE?

I'M HERE TO NEGOTIATE *PEACE* WITH GIDEON, FOR OUR PEOPLE, NOT TO GIVE INTO HIM.

I KNOW THIS IS CONFUSING AND VERY SCARY BUT YOU ARE PROTECTED BY AN ILLUSION. COME ON.

YOU PEOPLE ARE LISTENING TO CONSPIRACY THEORIES.

MY LEG. I THINK IT'S BROKEN.

LIAR!

IF YOU WEREN'T *AFRAID* OF THE TRUTH, WHY DO YOU CENSOR THE INTERNET IN OUR COUNTRY?

BECAUSE WE ARE ONLY SAFE--*ALL OF US*--IF WE KEEP OUR SECRETS. *PLEASE!* THINK ABOUT WHAT YOU'RE *DOING!*

ANYTHING YOU REVEAL YOU CAN *NEVER* TAKE BACK. IF YOU BRING IN THE UNITED NATIONS....

OUR PEOPLE ARE DOOMED.

IT'S GOING TO BE OKAY.

LEAN ON ME.

JUST A LITTLE BIT MORE. YOU, BY THE DOOR. WHEN THE TIME COMES, YOU HAVE TO CARRY HER OUT.

YOU HAVE TO BELIEVE ME.

WE'LL SEE WHAT THE UNITED NATIONS SAYS ABOUT OUR SECRETS WHEN THEY SEE THEM.

I'LL SEE YOU DEAD BEFORE I LET THAT HAPPEN.

HOW DARE YOU!

ENOUGH OF THIS! KILL HIS DAUGHTER. SHE'S A FREAK ANYWAY.

SAY GOODBYE TO WHAT YOU HOLD MOST DEAR.

TO BE CONTINUED...

115

CHAPTER ④

The greatest weakness of the Mantamaji is their uniqueness. The power that sets them apart can distance them from their friends and allies. And once they are alone, the Mantamaji can be destroyed. The darkness knows this. It treasures oblivion.

SHOOT HIM!

BOOF

NYPD! DROP YOUR WEAPONS!

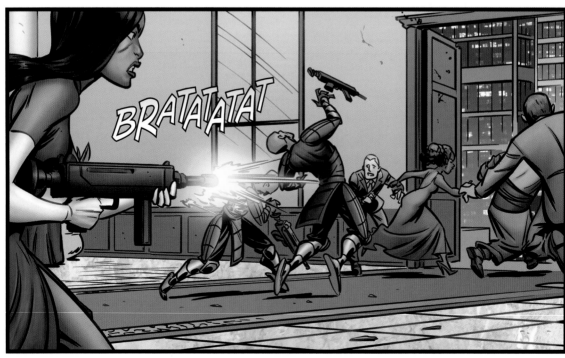

BRATATATAT

GET YOUR HANDS OFF ME!

HE'S TOO FAST!

GO! GO!

THUD

TAK

IT LOOKS LIKE, *YES*, THE HOSTAGES ARE *EXITING* THE BUILDING!

9

KEEP MOVING, CAREFUL, DON'T STOP.

YOU'RE OKAY, SIR.

ZWASHHH

MALA-NOTA.

ALI-A-KA-TAA.

POP

MALA-NOTA.

RATATTAT

KALEN-A-KA-TAA.

SWIP

THANK YOU.

RATATATATAT

WHAT THE--?!

HURRY! GO! GO!

HHIPP

THUD

FOLLOW ME!

CRKKK

FAL-A-HANAA

WATCH OUT!

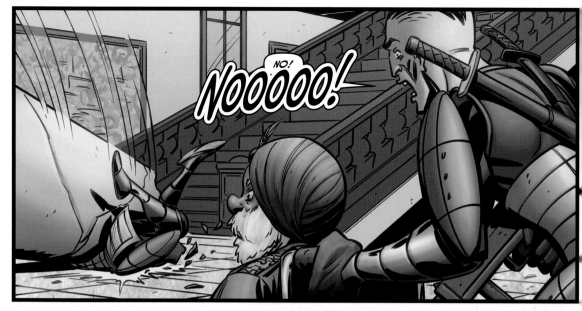

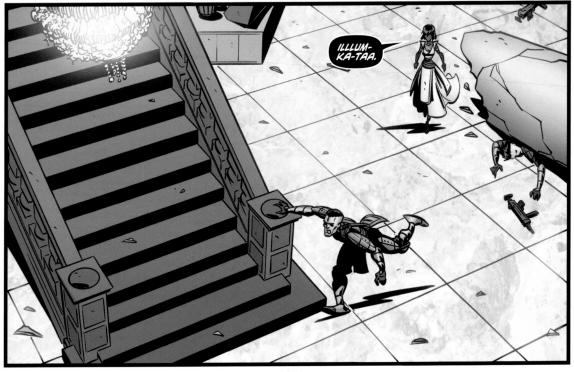

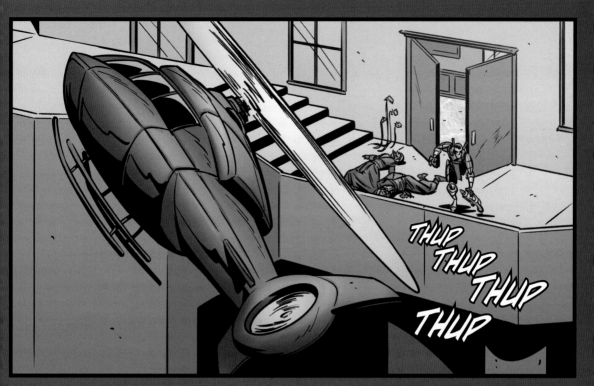

THUP
THUP
THUP
THUP

PAFF

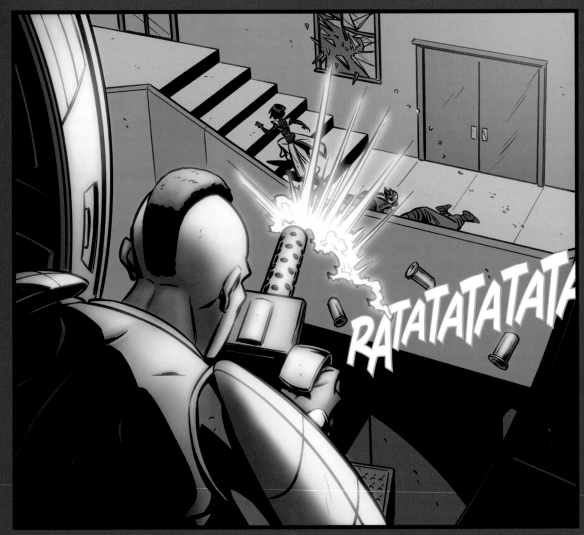

THUP THUP THUP THUP

THUP THUP THUP THUP

FOR OUR FAITH.

GRRGL

137

THANK YOU.

WAIT.

COME BACK.

CAN YOU TELL US WHAT HAPPENED? WHAT DID YOU SEE?

IT WAS THAT *MANTAMAJI.* HE SAVED US.

SPECIAL.

I BEG YOUR PARDON?

"SPECIAL." IT'S SUCH A STRANGE WORD, WHEN YOU THINK OF IT. IT MEANS YOU STAND OUT, BUT IT DOESN'T SAY WHETHER IT'S GOOD OR BAD.

YOU COULD BE A "SPECIAL" FRIEND WHICH IS GOOD, OR BE A "SPECIAL" PROBLEM, WHICH IS ONE THAT'S MORE DIFFICULT. IT COULD GO EITHER WAY.

ARE YOU SUGGESTING THAT *I'M* SPECIAL? OR THAT YOU ARE?

YOU'RE SPECIAL. I'M *UNIQUE.*

TWO OF WHAT SHE'S HAVING, PLEASE.

WHAT'S YOUR STORY?

WHAT DO YOU MEAN?

HUGO BOSS SUIT, FERRAGAMO SHOES, $100,000 ROLEX.

YOU DON'T LOOK LIKE THE TYPE THAT HAS TO TRY AND PICK UP WOMEN AT A BAR. ESPECIALLY NOT *THIS* BAR.

ALL THAT FROM A QUICK GLANCE?

IT'S A GIFT.

THAT'S VERY CLEVER OF YOU. BUT THAT'S NOT HOW I KNOW YOU'RE SPECIAL.

THEN HOW DO YOU KNOW?

IT'S A *GIFT*.

I'M NOT THE KIND OF GIRL WHO GOES HOME WITH MEN SHE MEETS IN BARS.

YOU JUST HAVEN'T MET THE RIGHT MAN.

AND THAT WOULD BE YOU?

IN THIS ENTIRE SHAMBOLIC TAPROOM, YOU'RE THE ONLY WOMAN WORTH TALKING TO.

ON THIS WHOLE BENIGHTED BLOCK, YOU BEAR THE ONLY HONEST LIGHT. ON THIS WHOLE--

HOLD THAT THOUGHT.

SORRY, NO TIME. WE'RE *FINISHED.*

BUT I DIDN'T GET TO EXPLAIN *WHY* YOU'RE SPECIAL.

THAT'S BECAUSE I DON'T *CARE.* ANYTHING YOU SAID WOULD BE A *LINE* ANYWAY.

IT'S YOUR *BLOOD.* ACROSS THIS ENTIRE CITY, YOUR BLOOD SINGS TO ME. AN *ANCIENT* SONG I'VE BEEN TRACKING FOR *DAYS.*

LOOK, MAN, IF YOU DON'T WANT TROUBLE, YOU NEED TO *STEP OFF. NOW.*

NOT WHEN I'VE FOUND WHAT I'M LOOKING FOR... *SANCTUANT!*

SHHH

GRAHH!

THUD

HNHH!

THOOM

WHAT ARE YOU?

I TOLD YOU.

WHAD

I'M UNIQUE.

EVEN MORE ANCIENT THAN YOU. SOMETHING DARK AND DIFFERENT.

AWOOOOOOOOOOOO

OOOOOOOOOOOOOOOOO

WHAT WAS THAT?

SOMETHING *BETTER*.

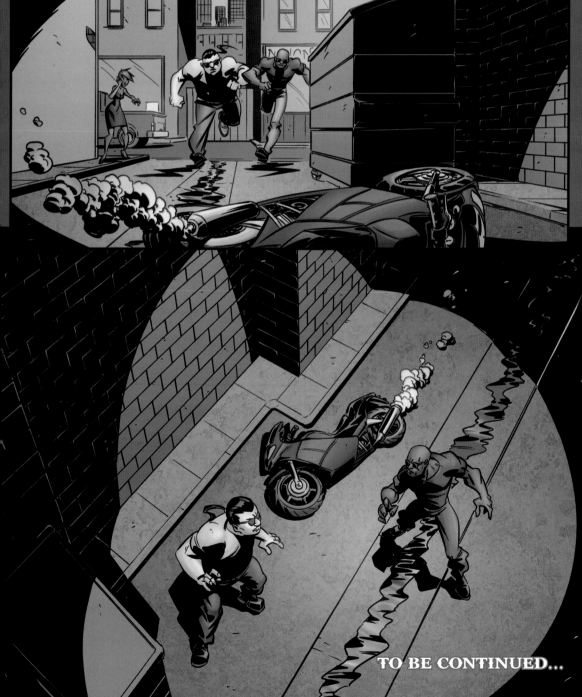

TO BE CONTINUED...

CHICAGO, ILLINOIS

⚡HUFF⚡
⚡PUFF⚡

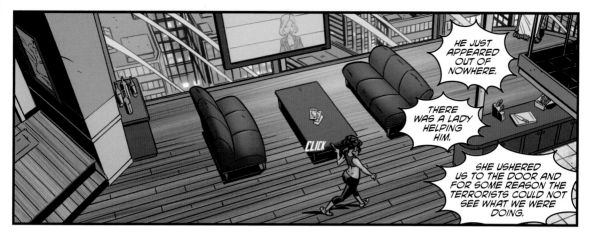

HE JUST APPEARED OUT OF NOWHERE.

THERE WAS A LADY HELPING HIM.

SHE USHERED US TO THE DOOR AND FOR SOME REASON THE TERRORISTS COULD NOT SEE WHAT WE WERE DOING.

CLICK

THESE ARE JUST SOME OF THE EYEWITNESS REPORTS TO A POSSIBLE TERRORIST ATTACK AT AN EMBASSY IN NEW YORK CITY TONIGHT.

GWRRR

WHAT WE DO KNOW FOR SURE IS IN AN ATTEMPTED HOSTAGE SITUATION; A GROUP OF ARMED MEN AND WOMEN ATTACKED A FOREIGN LEADER.

WAIT, THIS JUST IN.

WE HAVE LEARNED THAT EVERYONE WAS SAVED BY THE FIGURE KNOWN AS THE MANTAMAJI.

POLICE ARE NOT CONFIRMING HIS APPEARANCE--

--BUT IF IT TURNS OUT TO BE TRUE THIS WOULD MARK THE SEVENTH SIGHTING--

--OF THE MANTAMAJI--

--SINCE THE GLOBAL TERRORIST EVENT AT HOPE'S TEMPLE TWO MONTHS AGO.

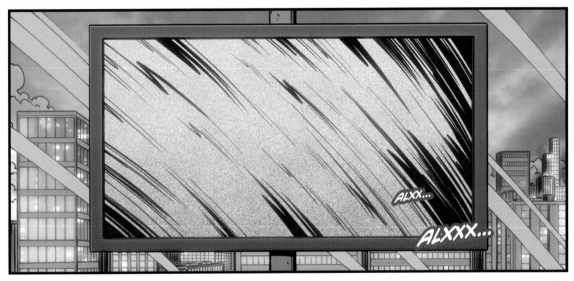

ALXX...

ALXXX...

CLICK

ALANA!

AHHHHHH!

SIRACH?!

ALANA.

CAN YOU SEE ME?

YOU MUST RELEASE ME!

RELEASE...

NO, THIS CAN'T BE HAPPENING.

CRK-CRRSSHH!

I NEED TO SPEAK TO HIM.

I DON'T CARE! PUT HIM ON THE PHONE!

NOW!

YOU SEE, MY DEAR. YOU ARE *SPECIAL*.

RING RING

...SO *SPECIAL* THAT YOU MAY *WITNESS* THE REPERCUSSIONS OF DISTURBING ME WHEN I'M ENTERTAINING.

I CAN'T STRESS HOW IMPORTANT THIS CALL BETTER BE.

REALLY?

PUT HER THROUGH.

EXCUSE ME, PLEASE.

156

TO BE CONTINUED...

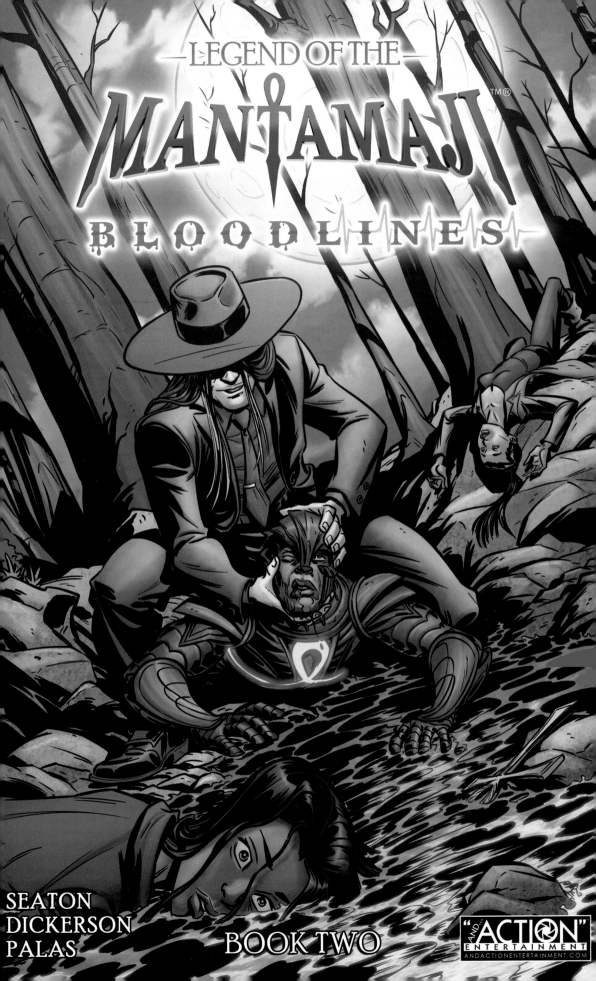

LEGEND OF THE MANTAMAJI: BOOK 1

Full color, 216 pages
ISBN: 978-1-930315-34-1

Elijah Alexander, New York's hottest, cockiest, and most media-hungry ADA, is about to learn something shocking: he is not even human. He's the last of the Mantamaji, a long-lost race of warriors who once protected humanity when the world was young. Now another Mantamaji—the worst of all their kind—has reawakened to visit doom on all of humanity.
Can Elijah accept his past, reject his present life, and learn about his talents, in time to defeat the villain who killed all the other Mantamaji before him?

LEGEND OF THE MANTAMAJI: BOOK 2

Full color, 188 pages
ISBN: 978-1-930315-37-2

In a single week, Elijah Alexander has gone from being a famous and successful ADA in New York, to a hunted, haunted renegade on a mission of vengeance. Because Elijah is the last of a race of ancient warriors called the Mantamaji who once fought the world's greatest evils. And now the greatest evil of all has just reappeared and seeks to destroy the world as we know it. Elijah's the only one who knows how to stop this, and the only one with the power to get it done—because it takes a warrior to kill a mystical being. Or four of them.

LEGEND OF THE MANTAMAJI: BOOK 3

Full color, 188 pages
ISBN: 978-1-930315-56-3

Beaten, betrayed, and left for dead, Elijah Alexander, the last Mantamaji, knows the end of the world is at hand. Soon Sirach will carry out his plan to open the Gates of Time and alter Earth's history to suit his purposes. How can Elijah stop Sirach, when he's already failed before? To succeed, he will have to put aside vengeance, ignore his pain, and listen to a wisdom he's forgotten. But he, and the world, are running out of time.

ANDACTIONENTERTAINMENT.COM

WWW.LEGENDOFTHEMANTAMAJI.COM

STORY BY ERIC DEAN SEATON
ART BY BRANDON PALAS
LETTERS BY DERON BENNETT
COLORS BY ANDREW DALHOUSE
AGE RANGE: 8+
GENRE: FANTASY/SUPERHERO/CRIME